An Honest Boy

Adapted by Jiang Zhenli
Illustrated by Hu Yongkai

DOLPHIN BOOKS   BEIJING

First Edition   1988

Hard Cover: ISBN 0-8351-1889-4
Paperback: ISBN 0-8351-1890-8

Copyright 1988 by Dolphin Books

Published by Dolphin Books
24 Baiwanzhuang Road, Beijing, China

Distributed by China International Book Trading Corporation
(Guoji Shudian), P.O. Box 399, Beijing, China

Printed in the People's Republic of China

In ancient times, there was a small country in the south where people were fond of flowers. They planted flowers everywhere, and the land looked like a sea of flowers and the air was sweet with the scent of flowers all the year round.

The king of that country also liked flowers very much. Even though he was king, he tended his garden every morning and evening.

As time went by, the king became old: His eyes turned farsighted; his hearing was lost; and his walk became unsteady. His days as king were numbered. He decided to choose a successor.

But who would his successor be, and how should the selection be made? As a flower lover, he decided to let a flower choose.

One day, the king issued an imperial edict: The children of the country come to the palace to get a flower seed. The child who can make the seed blossom within a year with the flower the king likes the best will be his successor.

This news caused great excitement throughout the land. All the parents wanted their children to be king, and all the children hoped they would be chosen.

Children from all over the
country swarmed into the
palace to get the flower
seeds.

The last child to come was Song Jin. He had got the news later than anyone else because he had been helping his father with some farm work in the fields. So he got the last seed.

Back home, Song Jin filled one of his best flowerpots with rich soil, and planted the seed carefully into it.

He watered it every day. How he hoped the seed would sprout, branch out, and blossom with beautiful flowers!

Day after day passed, but nothing grew in the pot.

Song Jin was very worried. He transferred the seed to a bigger pot.

He put in new rich black soil.

Another two months passed. Still nothing happened in the pot.

The day had come. The children put their nice clothes on, and their faces looked like flowers in their joy.

They rushed to the palace with their beautiful fresh flowers. There were red flowers, yellow flowers, purple flowers and white flowers. The children waited to be chosen.

Song Jin was ashamed of his empty pot. He thought that the other children would laugh at him because he didn't know how to grow a flower.

His clever young sister made a suggestion: "We have so many beautiful flowers here at home. Choose the best one and present it to the king."

Song Jin shook his head. "Those flowers were planted by our parents, not me. I can't pretend they are mine."

His father overheard them. He praised Song Jin and said: "Any child who practises fraud is not a good child."

Holding the empty pot in his hand, Song Jin went straight to the palace.

The king came out and looked at the flowers slowly, one by one.

How beautiful those flowers were! But the king, frowning, did not say a word.

He finally came to Song Jin, who was hanging his head, wondering whether he would be punished.

The king asked him, "Boy, why did you bring a pot without a flower?"

It turned out that one of the king's seeds had been cooked, so it couldn't possibly sprout and blossom. Song Jin had gotten just that one. He was an honest child, which the king appreciated very much.

A Magic Cart

Adapted by Jiang Zhenli
Illustrated by Hu Yongkai

DOLPHIN BOOKS   BEIJING

In a village cottage lived a little girl named Weng Lingling and her mother. Her father worked in a town.

Lingling was a sensible girl and often helped her mother with the household work.

One day, her mother was ill and couldn't get out of bed. Early that morning Lingling set out for the mountain to collect firewood. She thought while she was walking, "I'll collect a lot of firewood, and then I'll pick a bunch of fresh flowers to make my mother happy. And I'll catch a big fish and cook a bowl of fish soup to make my mother well again."

Just then, a rabbit jumped out of the grass! Very frightened, it ran to Lingling and said, "Sister Lingling, help me! That eagle is going to eat me!"

Lingling quickly picked up a stone and threw it at the eagle. The eagle was frightened away.

To thank Lingling, the rabbit took out many toys from his cave for her.

"Thank you very much," said Lingling, "but I don't have time to play with them. I have to collect firewood and prepare medicinal herbs for my mother."

"Sister Lingling, I'll give you a cart that will help you in your work." At that, a small cart pulled by eleven tiny horses appeared in front of Lingling.

Lingling accepted it gladly, but she wondered how she could get into such a small cart! At that, the cart suddenly grew big, and the eleven horses as well.

Happily, Lingling climbed into the cart and said to the horses, "Please drive me to a place with a lot of firewood."

The eleven horses raised their heads and whinnied. In the twinkling of an eye, they arrived at the mountain.

Lingling was very pleased to see that there was firewood everywhere. She gathered it quickly and the cart was soon filled up.

It was still early, so Lingling thought she would find an interesting place to play for a while. Immediately the eleven horses began to run.

They drove her to a beautiful place.

She plucked flowers while she was singing. Finally she had a whole bunch of pretty flowers to present to her mother.

Then she caught a carp in the river so she could make her mother some nourishing soup.

Lingling wanted to go home. The horses had already read her mind and began to pull the cart. Ding ling ling. . . ding ling ling. . . . Suddenly she caught sight of an old woman weeping at the side of the road.

Lingling stopped the horses and asked, "Grandma, why are you weeping?" "My daughter is dying of illness, and the doctor said that the smell of fresh flowers can help her," the old woman replied.

"Grandma, don't cry. I give you this bunch of flowers." So saying, she put the bouquet in the woman's hands.

But the old woman still wept. "The flowers are not enough. She needs to eat a big carp too."

Lingling gave her fish to the old woman. But the woman still wept with grief.

"Grandma, why do you still weep?" Lingling asked. The woman replied, "The doctor told me that to save my daughter's life the carp should be cooked with a full cart of firewood."

"Grandma, I give this cart of firewood to you. Please climb on!" The horses started running, and they soon arrived at the old woman's house.

The daughter of the old woman smelled the flowers and then ate the carp cooked with the firewood. She recovered completely.

The daughter of the old woman and Lingling became good friends. The old woman was very grateful to Lingling and invited her to stay for a few days. But Lingling insisted on going home to see her mother immediately.

On the way back Lingling ran into the rabbit again. The rabbit asked her, "Where are your firewood, flowers and carp?" Lingling told him the whole story.

When he heard what had happened, the rabbit called his friends together and ran back to the mountain. Soon all the rabbits returned, bringing a lot of firewood, a carp, and a bunch of flowers and put them on the cart.

Then the cart drawn by eleven horses went directly to Lingling's house. After smelling the flowers, her mother could sit up; and after eating the carp that Lingling had cooked with a cart of firewood, she was completely well again.

I'm
not a
BEAR

DENISE BURT
photography by
RON RYAN

BUTTERCUP BOOKS

I'm not a bear!

A lot of people think that koalas are bears,
but we are not.
We are marsupials.

Koala mothers like this one have a warm pouch in which her baby lives for the first six to eight months of its life. Then the baby rides on its mother's back for a few more months.

This one is nearly a year old, so he'll soon be looking after himself.

Koalas are related to the wombat. Wombats are marsupials too. They are ground animals and eat roots and grass.

Koalas live in the tops of eucalypt trees and eat the tender leaves.

The good leaves are often a long way up. There's not much to eat on this branch.

After all that climbing and eating we sometimes fall asleep right where we are . . .

or settle down to a good scratch.

Crossing the road in wildlife reserves can sometimes be dangerous.

Some drivers forget to watch out for us. We are a "protected species".

Koalas are better at climbing trees than crossing roads.
Our sharp claws make it easy to go straight up . . .

and hold on when we get where we want to be.

Our claws also make it easy to hold on and eat at the same time.

And they are wonderful for those itchy spots.

We don't need much water.
There is all we need in the nice juicy eucalypt
leaves like these.
In the early morning they have cool dew drops on
them too.

We don't need many teeth either, though a good strong tongue helps.

There's nothing to eat here.
Jumping into the next tree is quicker than going down and up again.

Some of us aren't so good at jumping yet. It's a long way to fall.

Life is usually peaceful until there are too many koalas in one place.
Then the Wildlife Rangers have to move some of us to another area.

We don't like being moved so we snarl and grunt.
But they don't hurt us. They take us in sacks to a
place where there's more food. And we like that!

There always seems to be a lot of visitors.
Koalas are very popular.

But sometimes the people come too close.

We often pretend we're asleep and hope the visitors will go away.

But the little ones are curious and won't sit still.

It's sometimes hard to find a warm quiet spot for a sleep.

Ah . . . that's perfect.

Look who's here!
It wasn't such a quiet spot after all . . .

And it's windy too!

Koalas are

sometimes itchy,

sometimes sleepy,

sometimes busy,

sometimes grumpy,

but we are **never** bears.

KOALAS
Phascolarctos cinereus

The word 'koala' comes from an Aboriginal dialect and means 'no water'. The Aborigines observed that the koala did not need water as other animals did.

The koala is born blind and hairless when it is not much bigger than a bean, at about five weeks. It wriggles through the mother's fur to her pouch. The mother helps this grub-like creature by licking her fur to provide a 'path' to her pouch.

Once inside the pouch, the baby attaches itself to one of the two milk teats. It stays in the pouch for about six months, where it develops thick fur, powerful legs and claws. As it grows bigger and stronger, it pops its head out of the narrow vertical opening to the pouch.

When the baby is strong enough to leave the pouch, it climbs on to its mother's back. Even with a baby in this position, the mother can move easily from tree to tree. The baby's strong claws grip the mother's thick fur firmly and ensure a safe ride.

The koala's front paws have the thumb and first 'finger' close together, with the other three making up a second section. The toes on the hind legs are separated and both front and hind paws have soft padded soles, making them ideal for climbing and holding.

Koalas are found in coastal areas throughout north eastern and southern Australia. The northern koalas are slightly smaller than those in the south and their fur is shorter and not as thick to enable them to cope with the hotter climate in the north.

Although passive by nature, koalas will defend themselves if cornered. They assume a squatting position and make boxing motions with their forearms, slashing wildly. Their razor-sharp claws could rip a man's skin to the bone.

The koala is protected by law, but it was not always so. In the early days it was hunted and killed for its thick fur. In the early 1920's, over 2 million pelts were sent out of the country. In addition to the unlimited killing for their fur, the koala numbers were reduced by bushfires, disease and land clearing. The koala came very close to being wiped out completely. Fortunately it was realised in time that their numbers were down to a few thousand and steps were taken to halt the decline.

Hundreds of surviving koalas were relocated in areas where suitable trees were plentiful and their numbers began to increase. The law now deals very harshly with anyone who kills or injures a koala or who keeps one in captivity without permission. But even with this protection, large numbers die each summer in bushfires. Man has also passed on some of his own diseases — like the common cold — against which the koala has no immunity.

Constant care and protection are necessary to preserve this appealing little Australian marsupial which, like the kangaroo, has become a national symbol.